The Rumbustious Dragon
and other
Stories and Poems

Daphne Lister

The Rumbustious Dragon and other Stories and Poems

Illustrated by
CAROLINE McDONALD-PAUL

HODDER AND STOUGHTON
LONDON SYDNEY AUCKLAND TORONTO

For my mother and father,
who read to me when
I was very young

British Library Cataloguing in Publication Data
Lister, Daphne
  The rumbustious dragon and other stories and poems.
  I. Title   II. McDonald-Paul, Caroline
  821'.914   PZ8.3
  ISBN 0-340-38080-2

Text copyright © Daphne Lister 1986
Illustrations copyright © Hodder and Stoughton Ltd 1986

First published 1986

Published by Hodder and Stoughton Children's Books,
a division of Hodder and Stoughton Ltd,
Mill Road, Dunton Green, Sevenoaks, Kent TN13 2YJ

Photoset by Rowland Phototypesetting Ltd,
Bury St Edmunds, Suffolk

Printed and Bound in Great Britain by
T.J. Press (Padstow) Ltd, Padstow, Cornwall

Contents

The Rumbustious Dragon

Once upon a time there was a rumbustious young dragon called Rumbold. He had just learned to blow fire and smoke through his nostrils and was very pleased with himself.

'Come on,' he said to all the other young dragons, 'let's have a competition to see who can make the most fire and the most smoke.'

So they all puffed and blew until the grass was scorched and the air was thick with smoke. Of course, Rumbold was the fieriest, smokiest dragon of all.

'Hurray! I've won the competition,' he called triumphantly and he began to chase all the other little dragons and tease them by singeing their tails and making them cough by blowing his thickest smoke in their faces.

'Stop it!' cried the more timid little dragons,

but rumbustious Rumbold went on teasing them until at last they all ran home and played quiet games like ludo and snakes-and-ladders and hunt-the-thimble.

Rumbold decided to go for a walk and see if he could find anyone else to play with. He hadn't gone far when he came to a small village. From the chimney of every house and cottage swirled blue smoke, for it was a cold day and everyone had their fires burning.

'I'll soon show them who can make more smoke than *that*!' said Rumbold and he flew up on to one of the rooftops and began blowing the smoke back down the chimney, plus a bit of his *own* smoke.

'Oh, my goodness!' said Mrs Smith as the smoke poured into her room. 'My chimney must need sweeping.'

By now Rumbold had moved to the roof next door.

'Oh, bother!' said old Mr Burton, coughing, 'the wind must be blowing from the north-east for the chimney to smoke like that.'

'Oh, dear!' said Mrs Neatly in the next cottage when Rumbold blew down her chimney, 'All my newly washed curtains and chair-covers are going to be *black*! I hope there isn't a birds' nest in the chimney.'

Everyone in the village looked in dismay at the smoke blowing down their chimneys. By this time Rumbold had reached the last house where Miss Popplewell, a retired schoolteacher, lived.

'Good gracious! Whatever's happening?' said Miss Popplewell crossly when *she* saw the smoke. She knew that *her* chimney didn't need sweeping because it had been swept the week before and she knew that no bird had had time to build a nest there since then and she also knew that the wind wasn't blowing from the north-east because she could see the weather-vane on top of the church from her living-room window.

Miss Popplewell went outside and looked up at the roof. If she was surprised to see Rumbold blowing down her chimney she didn't show it.

'Stop that!' she commanded sharply, 'And come down here *at once!*'

Rumbold looked down at Miss Popplewell. She seemed very cross. He thought he had better do as she said.

'Now,' she asked when he was standing in front of her, 'Just what do you think you are doing?'

'Well you see, we had a competition and I was the best at blowing smoke,' said Rumbold

' – and flames,' he added proudly.

Miss Popplewell frowned. 'Go inside!' she commanded, pointing to her front door.

Rumbold went into her cottage and in a moment he was coughing and his eyes were watering because of all the smoke.

'Nothing very clever about causing all *that*, is there?' Miss Popplewell asked sternly.

Rumbold shook his head sadly. 'I'm sorry,' he said, 'I didn't think.'

'You had better see if you can be best at putting things right,' said Miss Popplewell.

So Rumbold spent a very busy day going to every house in the village and he dusted and he mopped and he washed windows and he helped Mrs Neatly to wash her curtains and chair-covers again and hang them on the clothes-line and he was so tired by the time he had finished he didn't feel nearly as rumbustious as he usually did.

'Well done!' said Miss Popplewell, her eyes twinkling. 'Come and have something to eat now.'

So Rumbold went and had a very nice tea at Miss Popplewell's house and then she showed him all the books in her bookcase. Some had beautiful pictures in them. She even read him a story.

'I wish *I* could read,' Rumbold sighed when she had finished.

'I'll teach you,' said Miss Popplewell, smiling.

So Rumbold learned to read and he read fairy tales and school stories and funny stories and sad stories but best of all he liked exciting adventure stories.

And sometimes he read to all the other little dragons and they didn't run away from him any more because now that he had learned to read he was never *quite* as rumbustious again.

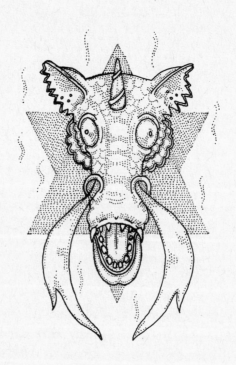

The Wind Witch

The wind witch is coming,
The wind witch is coming,
Listen! Can't you hear her
Sighing and humming?
Soon, through the wood
She'll come screaming and moaning,
All the trees will be bending
And creaking and groaning.

When the wind witch flies through,
With her broom she'll come rushing,
Stripping leaves off the trees
With her sweeping and brushing,
Red, yellow, gold,
They'll be spinning and dancing,
Listen! The wind witch
Is quickly advancing . . .

Whoooo, Whooooooo, WHOOOOOOOO!

The Rainbow Shell

Somewhere, somewhere in the deepest part of the sea, lies the rainbow shell. It is a very wonderful shell for it can bring about remarkable changes to the lives of those who are lucky enough to find it. But only once in a hundred years do the drift of the tide and the pull of the moon lift it from the sea-bed and carry it to one of the world's many shores, where it may be discovered by someone searching for they know not what as they pass along.

Once, long ago, a young girl in a far-off land was looking for fish at the edge of the sea. Her heart was heavy, for her mother was very ill and no longer able to work in the hot fields from sunrise to sunset. Because of this, not only were they starving for lack of food, they were in danger of being turned out of the tiny shack

14

where they lived, for the landowner who employed them was a hard man, only interested in those who were strong enough to labour and earn money for him. He gave little in return – only poor dwellings and a meagre supply of food.

Tears filled the girl's eyes as she remembered that that very day the landowner would be coming to the hut and she knew how angry he would be when he discovered that her mother was too ill to work. What was to become of them, she wondered helplessly?

And then, through her tears, she saw the unmistakable colours of the rainbow. She rubbed her eyes and there, in front of her, she saw the rainbow shell.

She picked it up and looked at it. It was beautiful. She liked the feel of it, too. It was soothing, somehow. Then she held it to her ear and listened. She couldn't describe what she heard. It wasn't music, it wasn't voices, and yet she seemed to hear *something*! And suddenly she felt hope again in her heart. She forgot her hunger and ran back to the little hut.

'Look what I've found!' she said, going to where her mother was lying and holding up the shell for her to see.

Light seemed to come into the sick woman's

eyes when she saw the shell, and she reached out a thin, tired hand to touch it. Her fingers closed around the shell and she fell asleep, smiling peacefully.

Not long afterwards the landowner arrived, a whip in his hand.

'Why aren't you working?' he demanded harshly.

The girl cowered a little but said bravely, 'My mother is very ill. She cannot work and she needs me to look after her.'

The man gave a roar of displeasure which woke the sick woman. At the same moment he noticed the shell in her hand.

'What is that?' he asked.

The girl's mother held it out to him.

'Here . . . keep it,' she whispered with a smile.

He snatched it from her and examined it as the girl and her mother had done before. While he turned it over in his hand something compelled him to look at the sick woman and her thin, sad-faced daughter and suddenly for the first time in his life, he wondered what it was like to be somebody else – somebody less fortunate than himself. And he felt pity mingled with shame.

'I will send a doctor to see you,' he told the

woman, awkwardly, for he wasn't used to being generous. 'In the meantime, rest quietly and forget your worries.'

The girl's eyes filled with tears of joy at his unexpected kind words.

'Oh, *thank* you!' she cried, running to him and hugging him. Then, taking one of his large hands in her small dark ones, she kissed it gently.

The man was surprised – surprised, too, at the great joy he felt in his heart, and tears came into *his* eyes. It was within his power to bring happiness to many people, he thought, as he looked again at the shell.

Not only did the landowner send baskets of food for the girl and her mother until they were both well and strong, but from that day, he treated all his workers differently – fairly – and cared for them as though they were his children and they grew to love and respect one another and happiness spread through all their hearts.

The man kept the shell for the rest of his life and cherished it, but what a pity he did not pass it on, for after he died it was lost for some years. When it was found again, covered in dust, it was put with some other old shells and thrown back into the sea.

Of course, every hundred years, it was

washed up again and brought happiness to others who were lucky enough to find it. To the family who, although rich, were always quarrelling, the shell brought understanding and tolerance. To the doctor, worried about performing a difficult and dangerous operation on one of his patients, it brought confidence and the power of healing which stayed with him all his life and enabled him to help hundreds and hundreds of sick people who had given up hope. But somehow, the shell itself was lost again and eventually put back into the sea.

The last time it was washed up on one of the earth's shores, it was thrown back again almost immediately by the leader of an invading army who had come across the sea to try and conquer new lands. The leader had no time for things like beautiful shells and as he walked up the beach from his boat he kicked it into the sea. Only as it rose through the air and its rainbow colours shone in the sunlight and dazzled him for a moment, did he realise that he had thrown away something wonderful – something better than all the lands and treasures in the world, and for the rest of his life he felt a great sense of loss. And though he searched and searched that shore and many more, he never saw the rainbow shell again, for of course, another hundred years must pass before it will be washed up by the sea once more.

Oh, if only the rainbow shell, the *next* time it is found, could be passed around the whole world, from hand to hand in every land, how different things could be! There could be an end to need and greed, sickness and suffering, wickedness and war. For everyone would possess that understanding which would bring joy and love and peace – the most wonderful treasures on earth – to all our hearts.

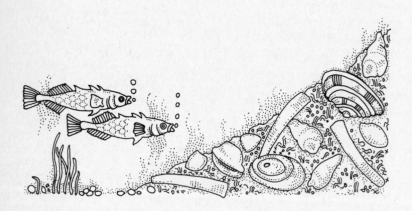

Wild White Horses

Listen to the thudding as the wild, white horses
Gallop over sands by the moonlit sea,
White manes flowing and white tails blowing
And their hoofbeats seem to say, 'We are free,
   we are free.'

A white moon shines on the wild, white horses
And casts its light on the wild, wide sea,
The horses go by prancing and the sea seems to
   be dancing
And the white waves whisper, 'We are free, we
   are free.'

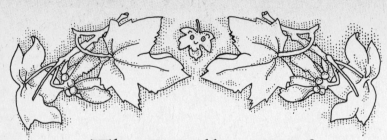

The Smallest Leaf

Once, in the middle of a park there was a large tree. Hundreds and hundreds of leaves hung from its branches but there was one that was smaller than all the rest. This leaf was on one of the lowest, innermost branches. It didn't often feel the warmth of the sun because it was over-shadowed by all the other leaves and it had to wait until the raindrops dripped down from leaf to leaf before it felt their soft, refreshing touch.

Sometimes, when the wind blew, the leaves rustled and sang songs of all the things they could see – birds and aeroplanes, the pond in the park and children playing, rooftops of houses and the church spire with its golden weathercock, and a river with a bridge across it.

'I wish *I* could see all those wonderful things,' the smallest leaf said with a sigh, trying to peep between all its brothers and sisters, but only occasionally did it get a glimpse of anything and then it was just a tiny chink of sky or a small patch of grass. How the little leaf wished it were a big leaf on the outside of the tree right at the top.

One day the leaves said, 'See, our colour is changing.'

It was true. They were gradually turning red.

'Oh, how beautiful. I wish *I* could become that colour,' said the smallest leaf. And soon, to its joy, it *did* turn red.

Some of the big leaves fell to the ground and made a red carpet under the tree.

'I expect *I* shall fall soon,' thought the smallest leaf a little sadly. 'If only I could have seen something of the world before it was time to go!'

Who knows? Perhaps the wind heard the smallest leaf. For that very day it came rushing through the park huffing and puffing and tugging at the leaves still left on the trees.

'Come and play,' it called. 'Come and dance. Whoooosh,' and it shook the leaves hard.

The smallest leaf felt itself pulled from its branch.

'Help!' it called, feeling afraid just for a moment. Then, as the wind lifted it, it realised that it was flying, up, up, high in the air. At last it could

see all the wonderful things it had heard about. The wind blew it over the pond and over the rooftops and right past the golden weather-cock on top of the church spire.

'What an adventure!' sang the small red leaf happily.

All morning the leaf twirled and whirled through the air, over the river and across the fields. It even tickled the nose of one of the cows as it went past and made it sneeze!

At last it came to rest in a lane. A little girl was walking along the lane with her mother. In her hand she had some different coloured leaves she had collected – brown, gold and yellow. Suddenly she saw the small red leaf lying on the path in front of her and bent down to pick it up.

'Oh, look!' she called to her mother. 'Look at this beautiful little red leaf. I *must* keep this one.'

So the smallest leaf was carried back to the little girl's home with the others and her mother showed her how to press them between the pages of a book so that they wouldn't curl up and die. When the little girl took them out of the book some days later, the smallest leaf was rather like paper but as red as ever. Then the little girl made a tree picture with all the pressed leaves and hung it on her bedroom wall.

'This is lovely,' thought the smallest leaf,

looking around the room. 'How lucky I am to have seen something of the world and now to have found a new home.' And it glowed happily as it felt the sun shining on it through the window.

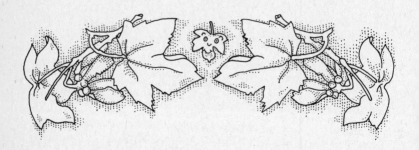

Miss Elcoate's Shop

Miss Elcoate's shop's a banquet,
Miss Elcoate's shop's a treat,
Miss Elcoate's shop's a party
With such lovely things to eat.

There's flapjack and there's frangipane
And doughnuts full of jam,
And apple pies and gingerbread
And flans with cheese and ham.

Sausage rolls and chocolate cake
And lovely crusty bread,
And licky-sticky currant buns –
A most inviting spread!

Miss Elcoate's shop smells lovely,
All spicy, warm and sweet,
Miss Elcoate's shop's a banquet,
Miss Elcoate's shop's a treat.

Little Hippo gets Stuck

One morning Little Hippo got up very early and went to the park. It was so early that the big iron gates were still locked.

'Bother!' said Little Hippo and he peered through the railings to see if he could see Peter the park-keeper coming with the keys but there was no sign of him. Little Hippo pushed his head a bit further through the railings to get a better look up the path. Just then he heard children's voices behind him.

'Hallo, Little Hippo,' called Michael and Ann and Billy.

Little Hippo tried to turn round to see them but he couldn't.

'Oh dear!' he said.

'What's the matter?' asked the children.

'I'm not sure,' said Little Hippo, 'but I think

I'm stuck.' He tried to pull himself free again but couldn't.

'Yes,' he said sadly, 'my head's stuck between the railings.'

'Perhaps we could *pull* you out,' suggested Michael, 'if all three of us were to pull your tail *very* hard.'

'No,' said Little Hippo quickly, trying to shake his head and finding, of course, that he couldn't. 'No, I don't think that would work. Not with my very small tail.'

'Look, here's Peter the park-keeper coming,' said Ann. 'He'll know what to do.'

'What's going on?' said the park-keeper as he came up to them.

'Little Hippo's got his head stuck between the railings,' said the children. 'Can you help him to get it out?'

Peter the park-keeper looked thoughtful. 'I might be able to take the gate off its hinges,' he said, 'but then he would have to wear the gate like a collar so that wouldn't be much good.'

'No,' said Little Hippo sadly, 'it wouldn't.'

Just then Ann said, 'Look, here's Jack the sailor, perhaps he'll know what to do.'

'Wuthering winkles!' exclaimed Jack when he saw the predicament Little Hippo was in. He thought for a minute or two, then he said, 'I'm a strong chap. I wonder if I can bend those railings a bit?' and he pulled and he pulled and he pushed and he pushed until he was red in the face but nothing happened.

'No, that's not going to work,' he said at last.

'Here's an old lady coming,' said Billy. 'Perhaps *she'll* know what to do.'

When the old lady reached them they told her what had happened.

'*I* have an idea,' she said, opening her handbag. 'Sometimes my rings get stuck on my finger but if I rub a bit of handcream around them they come off easily. So if we rub some of this on Little Hippo's neck he should soon have his head free.'

But even though they used every drop of the old lady's handcream, Little Hippo couldn't get his head out of the railings.

'I hope you won't have to stand here for ever,' said Billy.

'So do I,' said Little Hippo and he shut his eyes very tight because he thought he could feel a tear trying to get out.

'Look,' said Michael, 'here's Sue the nurse. She might know what to do.'

'Poor Little Hippo,' said Sue the nurse, patting him gently. 'Your neck is a bit swollen with everyone trying to pull your head back

through the railings. Just stand very still and we'll call the Fire Brigade.'

'Why? I'm not on fire as well, am I?' asked Little Hippo.

'No,' said Sue, smiling, 'but the firemen will be able to cut the railings with some special equipment they have.'

Peter the park-keeper hurried across to the telephone box and just a few minutes later they could hear the fire engine and then it came zooming round the corner.

'Well I never!' said Fred the fireman. 'Just keep still, Little Hippo, and don't mind the noise. We'll have you free in no time.'

Everyone – everyone except Little Hippo, that is – watched while Fred sawed through the railings. At last there was a big hole.

'There you are,' said Fred.

'Hurray!' shouted Michael and Ann and Billy.

'Well done!' said Sue, Jack and the old lady.

Slowly Little Hippo moved back from the railings. He was free at last. 'Oh, goody!' he said, moving his head from side to side. 'Thank you *very* much.'

'Well,' said Peter the park-keeper, 'I think we all need a cup of tea after that. Come along, everybody.'

So they all went to Peter the park-keeper's house and his wife gave them tea and buns she had just taken out of the oven.

'You'd better not go putting your head through railings again,' said Fred the fireman.

'No,' promised Little Hippo, licking the crumbs of his third bun from his lips, 'I won't *ever* – not if I live to be a hundred.'

And he never did.

Little Hippo tries to Dance

One day, Little Hippo said to his mother, 'Mother, please will you teach me how to dance?'

His mother smiled and shook her head.

'Oh no, I couldn't,' she said. 'You see, I'm a hopeless dancer. I've always had four left feet.'

'Oh!' said Little Hippo in surprise, looking down at his mother's feet. They looked the same as any other hippo's to him. But before he could tell her this she said, 'Why don't you go and play in the sunshine?'

'All right,' said Little Hippo and he set off for the park.

Sitting on one of the park seats, knitting, was an old lady he knew.

'Hallo, Little Hippo,' she said, smiling.

'Hallo,' said Little Hippo. Then, eyeing the

knitting, he said, 'If you're not *too* busy, please will you teach me how to dance?'

The old lady looked in surprise. 'Well,' she said, 'it's a long time since *I* did any dancing but I think I can remember how to waltz.'

She put down her knitting on the bench and went on to the grass. '*One*, two, three, *one*, two three,' she counted, showing Little Hippo the steps and humming a waltz tune.

Little Hippo tried it but he didn't think *that* was the kind of dance he wanted to do.

Just then Jack the sailor came walking briskly along the path.

'Hallo there!' he called. 'Whatever are you doing now, Little Hippo?'

'I'm trying to dance,' said Little Hippo.

'You would be better trying the hornpipe then,' said Jack. 'Look, I'll show you,' and he began to whistle a tune and dance a hornpipe.

Little Hippo tried to do the same but the steps were a bit tricky and he kept falling over his feet.

Just then Sue the nurse came along.

''Hallo,' she said. 'What are you doing?'

'Jack's trying to teach me to dance the horn-pipe,' said Little Hippo, 'but I'm not getting on very well,' he added as he fell over his feet again.

'Disco dancing's a bit easier than that,' said Sue. 'Look, I'll show you,' and she started to sing a song and shake and dance to the tune.

'This is easier,' said Little Hippo, shaking his head and waggling his body. But it wasn't really the kind of dance he wanted to do.

Just then Ann and her brother Michael and their friend Billy came running along on their way from school.

'Hallo,' they shouted, 'What are you doing?'

'Sue's teaching me to disco-dance,' said Little Hippo between shakes.

'We know a better dance than that,' said Ann. 'We learnt it at school.'

'Yes,' said Michael, 'The eightsome reel. It's terrific.'

'Oh, yes,' said the old lady, smiling. 'I always liked the eightsome.'

'So did I,' said Jack the sailor.

'So did I,' said Sue the nurse.

'Well, why not teach Little Hippo?' said Ann.

'Yes,' everyone said, smiling.

'But we need eight people and there are only seven of us,' Michael remembered.

'And we haven't any music,' said Billy.

Everyone looked glum.

Just then Peter the park-keeper came out of his house by the gate.

36

'Hallo, there, what's wrong?' he asked when he saw all the sad faces. So they told him their problem

He smiled. '*I* know the eightsome reel,' he said. 'I'll join in. And what's more I've got a record of the music. I'll just go and put it on and open the window wide so that we can hear it outside.'

A few minutes later they had all joined hands and were dancing around in a circle. It didn't take Little Hippo long to learn the whole dance with seven people to teach him.

When they had finished he glanced down. He was *very* glad *he* hadn't four left feet, like his mother.

'That must be the best dance in the world,' he said, smiling happily. 'Shall we do it again?'

And of course, they did.

The Princess and the Bells

Once an old fortune-teller told a king and queen that they would have a daughter and that bells would bring her great happiness.

Sure enough, less than a year later, a little princess was born. The king and queen were delighted.

'She shall be called Bellina,' said the king and he ordered all the bells in the kingdom to be rung as a sign of rejoicing.

But all the time the bells were ringing the baby princess cried. She didn't even seem to like the little silver bells that hung above her cradle.

'Poor Lina!' said her old nurse, shaking her head sadly at the baby princess.

'I don't understand it,' said the king, looking puzzled. 'The old fortune-teller said that bells would bring her happiness.'

The queen laughed. 'Yes, but our daughter is

too young yet to appreciate such things. You must wait until she is older.'

This gave the king an idea. He ordered new bell-towers to be built on all the public buildings in the kingdom and bells of all shapes and sizes and sounds were hung in these.

'We will make sure there are plenty of bells for her to hear,' he said enthusiastically. 'We will make this a kingdom of bells.'

It took several years for all the towers to be built and the bells installed. By this time the princess had grown to be a lovely girl with a happy, sweet nature.

Soon it was to be her birthday.

'We will have all the bells in the kingdom rung for the entire day, as a surprise for our daughter,' the king told the queen. Sure enough, from sunrise on the princess's birthday the bells pealed out.

Now Bellina didn't like the sound of bells at all, but she knew that her parents would be disappointed if she told them this after all the trouble they had taken and because she was so kind she couldn't bring herself to do so. So, though her head ached, she tried to smile and appear happy, but she was glad when the day was over and the persistent clanging had ended. She lay on the couch in her room and closed her eyes.

THE PRINCESS AND THE BELLS

'Poor Lina!' whispered the old nurse, stroking the girl's forehead soothingly.

Because Bellina was such a sweet-natured, lovely girl, princes from far and wide wished to marry her and she received invitations to visit their kingdoms.

'Will you come with us?' Bellina asked her nurse.

But the woman shook her head. 'I am too old to go on such a long journey,' she said, 'and you won't be needing me much longer, now that you are to marry,' and she went away to her own little cottage in a quiet place by the sea and Bellina and her parents set off to visit all the kingdoms to which they had been invited.

Now rumours about the fortune-teller saying that bells would bring Bellina great happiness had spread, and of course, as each prince wanted to please her the most, each one had had elaborate bell-towers built and bells that rang and pealed and chimed and played tunes!

But the princess didn't care for any of the princes and she certainly didn't like *any* of the bells. Her head ached continually.

At last the king and queen and their daughter returned home.

'Bellina looks so pale and ill,' said the queen. 'The journeying has been too much for her.'

41

So a message was sent to the old nurse, asking her to come back to the palace to look after the princess for a while until she was better again, but the old nurse sent back a message saying, 'Let the princess come to me.'

'But it's such a lonely, quiet place,' said the king, shaking his head.

'Never mind,' said the queen. 'We will let her go.'

So the next day the princess arrived at the nurse's little cottage which stood by itself at the edge of the sea. The only other dwelling in sight was a small castle on a cliff not far away.

'Poor Lina!' said the nurse when she saw the princess's pale sad face, and she gave her some hot soup and then told her to rest.

The girl lay in a little bed in a white-painted room and the soft lapping of the waves on the shore outside sent her to sleep in no time.

When she woke up, the first thing she saw was a glass of delicate blue flowers on the table beside her bed.

'Oh, how beautiful!' she said in delight.

'Someone left them outside of your window while you were sleeping,' said the nurse.

'Who was it?' asked the princess, curiously, but the nurse shook her head and said she didn't know.

The princess got up and dressed quickly.

'I shall go and look for the person,' she said and she went out of the cottage and looked to right and left but no-one was there. Then she walked along the beach and presently she saw a young man beside a small boat.

'Did you see anyone go to the cottage over there and leave some flowers?' she asked.

The young man was rather shy and his cheeks turned a bit red as he said, 'I'm sorry, I know I shouldn't have done it but I was sorry there were no bells to ring a welcome for you.'

The princess began to laugh and told him how she hated the sound of bells.

Then *he* laughed. 'So do I,' he said. 'I prefer the sound of the sea and the wind whispering through the grasses.'

'So do I,' sighed the princess. 'Oh, I wish I could live in that castle over there and stay in this peaceful place for ever.'

Then the young man took her hand and kissed it and said, 'Why don't you? If you will marry me you could come and share my castle.'

Then Bellina blushed a little for she hadn't realised until then that the young man was a prince.

The old nurse saw them standing hand in hand, looking so happy, and she smiled. Then she looked at the blue flowers again.

'So bells *have* brought dear Lina happiness, after all!' She chuckled to herself. 'But who would have thought they would be the bells of a simple flower – harebells?'

The Waterfall's Song

Once, across the sea in Norway, that land of mountains, fjords and lakes, there lived a girl called Kristina. Her parents had died when she was very young and Kristina lived with her grandmother – or Bestemor, as they say in Norway – in a pretty little painted wooden house on the lower slopes of a mountain. She was very happy there. She helped her grandmother to cook and clean and to look after the garden and tend the goats they kept in a meadow beside the house. In summer, when the days were long and sunny and they had finished their work, they would sit outside the house, sewing or just looking down into the valley. In winter, when darkness crept up the valley in the early afternoon, they sat inside by the warm stove and knitted stockings and shawls and mittens.

Every week Kristina would go to the nearest village to do the shopping.

'Now don't take the path through the forest,' her grandmother would say, and then she would add, in a whisper, 'for you know there may be trolls lurking there.'

'Don't worry, Bestemor, I won't,' Kristina would answer, shivering a little as she thought of the trolls – the ugly little dwarfs with long, matted hair, who were said to dwell in the mountain and who waited to waylay people who strayed into the darkness of the forest. So although it would have been quicker to have taken the short cut through the wood, Kristina always went the long way round.

One day, when Kristina returned from her shopping expedition, she was surprised to find a dark-haired stranger in the house.

'This is Ragnar, a distant relative of ours,' explained grandmother. 'He wants to stay here for a while because he has nowhere else to go.'

'Of course, Bestemor,' said Kristina, giving a little curtsy and smiling shyly at the stranger. But when she looked into his eyes her smile vanished because she saw only darkness and hate. He had come, not knowing of her existence, hoping the old lady would adopt *him* and eventually give him her house and land.

Already he was jealous of Kristina.

From that day he made her life a misery. He found fault with everything she did. He tried to turn her grandmother against her. Once, he even hid the old lady's brooch in a cupboard in Kristina's room to make her think her grand-daughter had stolen it. Of course, the old lady knew Kristina would not do such a thing. She, too, saw that Ragnar was a dark-hearted one and wished he would go away but she dared not tell him to do so for she was afraid of him.

Kristina was very unhappy and often cried herself to sleep at night.

'If only Ragnar had not come here,' she said to herself. 'He has destroyed all our happiness.'

One day, she was getting ready to go shop-ping when Ragnar said, 'Don't be away too long. There is much work to be done here. Take the short cut through the forest.'

'No,' said Bestemor. 'She is not allowed to go that way. There may be trolls in the forest.'

'Trolls? What nonsense!' Ragnar laughed darkly.

Kristina quickly left the house.

'I won't go through the forest,' she said to herself, 'but I will take a different path, the one that goes *behind* the forest. It is steeper but maybe it will be quicker.'

She set off along the track up the mountain-side. Eventually she came to a beautiful water-fall cascading down the rocks. It swirled and bubbled into little pools.

'How lovely!' said Kristina. 'It sounds like music.' She closed her eyes and the sound of the waterfall seemed more like music than ever. In fact, she seemed to hear it singing:

'From my waters, cool and deep,
Drink and you will fall asleep,
All will be revealed in dreams
To those who sip these crystal streams.'

Kristina was curious. Certainly the clear, sparkling water looked tempting. She cupped her hands, took some and drank. It was cool and lovely. She sipped some more. A pleasant drowsiness came over her. She lay down on the grass and was soon fast asleep.

When she woke up again the dream was still fresh in her mind. She had learned that Ragnar was plotting to kill her. She must not go back. There was someone who would protect her – she had seen him in the dream – someone with hair the colour of ripe corn and a kind smile. But where was he? She looked around. There was no-one.

She got up. She would go on to the village. Perhaps someone there would help her. But first, she took a little bottle that had once contained eau-de-cologne, from her pocket and filled it from the waterfall. Maybe it would be of use sometime.

She had only walked a short way when she heard the distant rumble of thunder and felt some drops of rain. She must find somewhere to shelter – but where? There was only the forest. Cautiously, she made her way to the edge of it and sheltered under the trees, but as the raindrops came faster and heavier, she was forced to go further into the wood where the trees grew more closely together, to keep her dry.

And then they came, silently at first, out of the shadows and from behind the trees, about twenty small, ugly creatures, hair almost covering their faces.

Kristina screamed but there was no-one to hear her. The trolls cackled and laughed and looked uglier than ever. They danced clumsily round her, pulling her hair and tweaking her nose, pinching and nipping her. All except one, Kristina noticed. He was uglier than all the rest but he didn't laugh and he didn't touch her.

At last the trolls led her away to a cave hidden

deep in the mountainside.

'You will be kept a prisoner until the moon is full,' said the chief troll. 'Then we will cast a spell over you and make you one of us.'

'No, no!' Kristina cried in horror. Once she had been turned into a troll there would be no escape. No-one would ever recognise her again.

Each night a different troll stood guard over her. At last, the evening before the full moon, it was the turn of the ugliest one of all, whom she had discovered was dumb and could not speak a word. Poor thing! She could hardly bear to look at him but she felt sorry for him and remembered he had not harmed her.

He brought her sweet, juicy berries and a cup of water.

'Oh, *thank* you!' she said, smiling at him. She could just see his eyes through the tangle of hair – they were kind eyes, not cruel like those of the other trolls.

The cup of water he had given her reminded her of the waterfall. Suddenly she seemed to hear its song again:

'From my waters, cool and deep,
Drink and you will fall asleep,
All will be revealed in dreams
To those who sip these crystal streams.'

Then she remembered the little phial of water in her pocket and an idea came to her. She took it out and refilled the cup.

'Drink this,' she said, handing the cup to the dwarf.

He did not hesitate but drank every drop. A moment later he yawned, rubbed his eyes and lay down to sleep. As he slept he changed slowly, slowly, from a wizened, ugly, little troll, into a fine young man with hair the colour of ripe corn.

Kristina gasped with astonishment.

'The young man in my dream!' she said.

Then Rolf Brave-Heart, for that was his name, woke up and smiled at Kristina.

'You undid the spell,' he said in delight.

'Yes,' Kristina said. 'But how can we escape?'

'Don't worry,' said Rolf, 'I saw how in my dreams. The trolls are having a party tonight to celebrate the coming of the full moon. We must wait until they have all eaten and drunk so much that they fall into a deep sleep. Then we can make our escape.'

And that is just what they did. Once out of the cave they ran down the mountainside together in the moonlight until they came to the little painted house.

'Bestemor! Bestemor!' called Kristina and the

old woman hurried to greet them, her eyes full of tears, and took them into the house. How horrified she was to hear of Kristina's adventures but how glad that her grand-daughter had found a kind, strong, young man like Rolf Brave-Heart to protect her in future.

And what of Ragnar, the Dark-Hearted one? He had his ear to the keyhole to hear their story. Afterwards he slipped away into the night. Maybe he went to drink from the waterfall and slipped down, down into the icy waters of the fjord below. Or maybe the trolls found him when they went out looking for Kristina and Rolf and took him prisoner. Maybe he just ran and ran as far away as he could because he was so full of shame he dared not face Rolf Brave-Heart. But one thing is certain. He was never seen in that part of Norway again. And Kristina and Rolf and Bestemor lived happily for the rest of their lives.

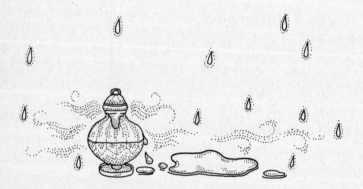

Waterfalls in Winter

Where the little waterfalls
Usually gush and play,
It is still and silent
If you go today.

Frost has stopped their singing games
Upon the watery stairs,
And music rooms among the rocks
Are changed to icy lairs.

As you look up the hillside,
All there is to see
Is a glistening, glassy staircase,
Sparkling silently.

Cuthbert Kitten's Winter Sleep

One autumn morning, Cuthbert Kitten was prowling around the garden and nosing into everything when he saw *another* nose. Actually, it was a snout – a little brown snout, snuffling its way out of a pile of dead leaves.

Cuthbert watched curiously. Then he saw two bright little eyes, then a little mound of brown prickles. It was a hedgehog.

'Hallo,' said Cuthbert Kitten, pleased to have company. 'Would you like to play a game?'

'Game?' said the hedgehog with a yawn. 'Oh, dear, no! This is no time for games.'

'Why not?' asked Cuthbert, pouncing on a leaf that was blowing past. *He* thought any time was a good time.

'Because I'm getting ready to go to sleep,' said the hedgehog.

Cuthbert blinked in surprise. 'You're going to sleep?' he asked. 'But why? It's not bed-time, it's morning.'

'No, no,' said the hedgehog, 'I don't mean *that* sort of sleep. I mean my long winter sleep. All hedgehogs go to sleep for the winter, you know, and so do some other animals as well.'

'You mean you go to bed for the whole winter?' asked Cuthbert.

'That's right,' said the hedgehog. 'First I have lots and lots and lots to eat, then I find a nice snug place like that pile of leaves there and I curl up until spring comes again. It's lovely not having to go out in the cold and the snow.'

'*I* don't like the snow,' agreed Cuthbert Kitten.

'There you are then,' said the hedgehog. 'Now, if you'll excuse me, I must be on my way. Talking about my winter sleep has made me eager to get settled down.' He yawned sleepily and shuffled back under the pile of leaves.

A few days later a cold wind was blowing.

'My!' said Annie at breakfast time, 'it's awful cold this morning.' She buttoned up her thick cardigan. 'I shan't be surprised if we get some snow today.'

Sure enough, a little while later the snowflakes began to fall.

Cuthbert Kitten sat on the windowsill and pretended to catch the flakes that settled on the glass, but he didn't think it a very good game. He liked to go outside – but not in the snow. He didn't like that horrible wet cold stuff at all. He thought about the hedgehog sleeping snugly under the pile of leaves. Perhaps it wasn't a bad idea to go to sleep for the winter.

The more Cuthbert thought of the idea the more he liked it – especially the bit about having lots and lots and lots to eat first. He licked his lips and went to see what he could find in the kitchen.

Annie was in the middle of cleaning out the fridge so there were lots of tasty dishes around and luckily she had gone into the other room to answer the telephone and was now having a long chat with one of her friends.

Cuthbert Kitten wasted no time cleaning out the dishes – smoked salmon paté, followed by the left-overs of yesterday's steak and kidney pie, then a slice of ham. There was even a little cream to finish with. Cuthbert Kitten licked his lips. All that should last him until spring, he thought. He yawned. Now all he had to do was find a nice cosy place to settle down for the winter, some-where where he wouldn't be disturbed. *He* didn't fancy a pile of leaves very much. He had a much better idea – the airing cupboard!

Stealthily he made his way upstairs. What luck! Annie had left the door of the airing cupboard open a little way. Cuthbert was so full of food he could hardly jump up to the shelf where all the clean sheets and towels and pillow-cases were kept but he managed it at last and soon he was fast asleep, dreaming happily. He slept and slept for a long time. Then a noise woke him up. He looked around. Where was he? Then he remembered.

'I wonder if winter's over yet,' he thought to himself, stretching. 'I had better go and see.'

He made his way downstairs.

'Oh, *there* you are, Cuthbert Kitten, you villain,' said Annie who was sitting knitting. 'Well, don't come looking for any more food today, you bad thing, because you can't have any.' She shook a finger at him. 'If I'd got hold of *you* this morning . . .'

Cuthbert Kitten listened in surprise. *This morning?* Had he only been sleeping for part of *one day?*

He watched the ball of wool from Annie's knitting roll down to the floor and got ready to pounce on it. Here was the chance of a good game! He didn't think he would bother to go back to sleep again for the rest of the winter, after all. It might be all right for hedgehogs but *he* didn't feel a bit tired now and it was much more fun to play games every day!

Cuthbert Kitten's Very Noisy Morning

Very early one morning, Cuthbert Kitten was curled up in his basket dreaming happily, when suddenly he was awakened by a lot of noise outside. First there was a rumbling and then there was whistling and then clumping of feet and then there was a rattle bang, rattle bang BASH! It was the dustbin men.

'Bother!' said Cuthbert rather crossly, because in his dream he had just been going to eat a lovely juicy kipper and hadn't wanted to be disturbed just then.

He curled up again, shut his eyes very tight and tried to dream the same dream again. But what was that?

Drip-drip, plip-plip, drip-drop, plip-plop!

Cuthbert rolled over and pricked up one of his little ginger ears. Splish-splash, plink-plonk, drip–drip! One of the kitchen taps was dripping.

Cuthbert sighed. It was no use! He couldn't go to sleep again now. He stretched his little ginger paws and his claws and his legs and his body and his neck and his tail and yawned. Well, now that he was awake he might as well get up. He drank all the milk that was left in his saucer and then went outside and sniffed around the garden.

Bzzzzzzzzzzzzz, came a noise not far from Cuthbert's ear. Bzzzzzzzz. What was what? Cuthbert looked but couldn't see anything. He put his head a bit closer to the flowers and BZZZZZZZZZ, an enormous bumble bee crawled out of one of them and buzzed angrily round Cuthbert Kitten's head.

'Oh, dear!' said Cuthbert, running away from the bee as fast as he could.

He ran into the house and hid under the settee. Trrrrrr-tring, trrrrrrr-tring. Another noise made Cuthbert jump. It was only the telephone.

Annie came to answer it. 'Oh, *hallo* Alice,' Cuthbert heard her say. He sighed. He knew there was going to be an awful lot of clackety-clack, chattery–chat now! Wearily he slunk out of the room and climbed the stairs. Oh, good! Annie had left her bedroom door open when she had gone to answer the phone. He padded into the room and curled up in his favourite place – in the middle of Annie's soft bedcover. In no time at all he was fast asleep, dreaming again – but not for long.

Waaaaaaaaaaa-mmmmmmmmmm, waaaaaaaaaaaa-mmmmmmmm, waaaaaa-mmmmm, something moaned downstairs.

Cuthbert opened his eyes. Oh no! He knew *that* noise. It was the horrid monster that lived in the cupboard under the stairs. It was the vacuum cleaner!

Waaaaaaaaaaa-mmmmmmmmmm, waaaaaaaaaaaa-mmmmmmmm it moaned, giving little growls sometimes as it tried to eat things it wasn't supposed to. Cuthbert heard it coming upstairs.

Waaaaaaaaa-mmmmm, grun, grun, grun, shoooooo! the horrid thing said.

Cuthbert jumped off the bed. Annie wouldn't be very pleased if she found him here. He waited until Annie and the horrid thing were in the next room and then he hurried downstairs. He went into the kitchen to see if Annie had put some more milk in his saucer. She hadn't. But standing near it was an empty tin waiting to be put in the dustbin. Cuthbert accidentally knocked it over. It rolled across the floor.

'Ah, now here's a good game,' thought Cuthbert, getting ready to pounce on it. He pushed it

and rolled it around the kitchen floor. He sprang on it. He tossed it about. He jumped over it. He fell over it. My, what a good game it was!

Suddenly Annie came into the kitchen.

'Cuthbert Kitten, whatever are you doing?' she asked crossly. 'I've never *heard* such a noise. Come along – outside!' and she put Cuthbert out into the garden.

Sadly Cuthbert lay under the apple tree. Fancy Annie saying she had never heard such a noise when the whole morning had been *full* of noises! And he had *only* been playing one of his favourite games!

Cats know the Cosiest Places

Cats always find the warmest places,
Like airing-cupboards and half-packed cases,
A rug by the fire, a place in the hay,
The patch on the roof where the sun shines all
    day,
Yes, cats know the cosiest places.

Cats always find the softest places
To curl up and sleep with their paws round their
    faces,
A velvet cushion, the comfiest chair,
Or an eiderdown – you'll find them there –
Yes, cats know the cosiest places.

Belvedere Beetle's
Great Ambition

Belvedere Beetle was no ordinary beetle. He came from a royal household and the feet *he* scurried away from to avoid being squashed were royal feet. In fact, he didn't have to scurry away very often for the palace he lived in was *enormous* – it had 699 rooms – so there was plenty of room to wander about undisturbed.

One morning, Belvedere was making his way across the Blue Drawing Room ceiling when he stopped and sighed.

'Oh dear, oh dear!' he said.

'Why, what's the matter, Belvedere?' asked Serena Spider, who was busy making a web on one of the chandeliers.

'Oh,' said Belvedere, 'ever since I was a baby beetle in the basement and heard about the 699 rooms in this palace it has been my ambition to see them all. But it is taking me so long and I am getting so tired and I have only seen two hundred and twenty-six rooms up to now. I still haven't seen the Gold Sitting Room or the Library or the Banqueting Hall with the magnificent painted ceiling.'

'Well,' said Serena, 'if you're tired why don't you stay here? This is a *very* nice room.' She swung contentedly on her silvery thread.

'Yes, yes,' replied Belvedere. 'It is a charming room. It's just that . . . well, I *should* like to see all the other rooms, especially the Banqueting Hall with the magnificent painted ceiling.'

'Then you had better continue your journey,' said the spider, 'because it is going to take you a long time.'

'Yes,' agreed Belvedere, setting off in the direction of the Emerald Sitting Room. It was two whole days before he arrived there. He looked at the brilliant green walls and the gold ceiling.

'Delightful! But oh, dear! My poor feet!' he said to himself, 'I shall never finish my journey at this rate.'

'What's the matter, Belvedere?' asked Ferdinand Fly, buzzing up to him.

So Belvedere told him how much he wanted to see all the rooms in the palace, especially the

Banqueting Hall with the magnificent painted ceiling.

'If only I could fly, like you,' said Belvedere.

'Yezzzzzzzz,' said Ferdinand, 'but you can't and I can't carry you, old chap, because you're bigger and heavier than I am.'

Belvedere nodded and sighed.

Just then Ferdinand began to buzz excitedly. 'I've had an idea,' he said, 'There's a banquet and ball in the palace tonight!' Then he flew close to Belvedere and buzzed something in his ear.

Belvedere was so excited he nearly fell off the gold embroidered curtain he was standing on.

'Wait about here,' buzzed Ferdinand, flying lower down and near the cream and gold doors, 'at eight o'clock.'

At last the huge marble clock on the mantelpiece struck eight. The doors opened and a long line of butlers came in, each wheeling a silver trolley laden with gold and silver tureens and dishes. As one of the trolleys brushed the curtain he was on, Belvedere took his chance and crawled quickly on to it and hid under a lace doily.

The butlers moved forward into the next room, then the next, then the next, then, at last, into the huge Banqueting Hall.

Belvedere peeped out from his doily. He saw

the ornaments and the paintings and the chandeliers with hundreds of candles burning and the garlands of flowers and the silver and crystal.

He managed to crawl off the trolley and on to the wall and scurried up to the top of a pillar where he could see the magnificent painted ceiling more clearly.

'Oh!' said Belvedere, for it really *was* magnificent. Then he looked down at the orchestra playing and the dukes and duchesses and princes and princesses and kings and queens, wearing their fine evening clothes of silk and satin and velvet and dancing happily. But none of them were any happier than Belvedere as he tapped his feet in time to the music.

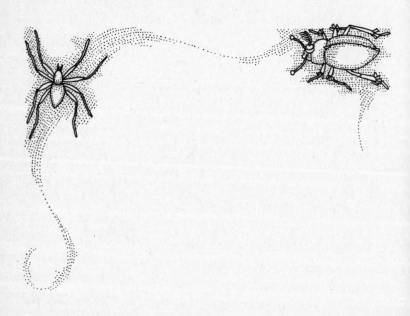

The Empty House

There are beetles in the basement
And woodworm in the stair,
Rats run in the rafters,
Mice are everywhere.

Once the windows used to shine,
The brasses used to gleam
And smoke curled from the chimney,
But now that's all a dream.

Poor old house,
With no-one left to care,
Just beetles in the basement
And mice everywhere.

The Princess who Loved Stars

Once there was a princess who loved stars. Every night she gazed up at them from her bedroom window. She liked the clear, dark, moonless nights best of all, when the sky was like black velvet and the stars shone like diamonds.

'Oh, how beautiful!' she would say delightedly.

Of course, some nights when it was cloudy or raining or foggy she couldn't see the stars at all and then she felt very sad.

One miserable winter the weather was particularly bad. Every night the stars were blotted out by mist and fog, cloud and rain. The princess grew sadder and sadder until she became quite pale and ill.

'If only I could see the stars again,' she said, 'I am sure I would feel better.'

So her father, the king, offered a reward to anyone who could bring back the brightness of the stars for his daughter.

As soon as the news got around, people began to arrive at the palace with their ideas. One had invented a huge machine like an enormous vacuum cleaner.

'This should suck up all the clouds and fog and make the stars visible again,' said the man who had invented it.

But the machine just made the fog and mist swirl around and didn't get rid of it at all.

The princess shook her head. 'No, it doesn't work. I still can't see the stars,' she said sadly.

The next person who came had a special, very long telescope.

'This should reach through the mist and fog,' he said confidently, as he set it up on the roof of one of the high turrets.

But when the princess looked up through the telescope she shook her head. 'No, it mustn't be long enough,' she said, 'I still can't see the stars.'

Other people came with their ideas but none of them worked. And then a young man arrived. In his hands he carried a medium-sized box.

'Show us your invention,' commanded the king and the young man opened the box. Inside were some small tubes.

'They aren't anything like stars,' the princess said, almost crying with disappointment for she liked the young man and had felt sure he would be able to show her the stars.

Then the young man smiled and asked if he might take the box outside into the palace gardens.

'All right,' said the king, wearily.

The princess looked through the huge window and watched curiously as the young man made his way across the garden. It was a grey, damp evening with not a star in sight. There was a tiny flicker of light as the young man struck a match, then the light went out. For a few moments nothing happened, then suddenly there was a fizzing noise and several stars – coloured stars – appeared in the dark sky. Each one burst into a shower of beautiful golden sparks.

The princess was delighted. 'How beautiful!' she cried.

There was another fizzing noise. More stars appeared – silver this time. Then came more – green and red and gold, falling from the darkness like shooting stars, then more and more, bursting and burning brilliantly. The air was filled with a delightful sharp scent.

At last the display was over and the young man came inside.

'Oh, thank you,' said the princess, her eyes shining as brightly as any stars. 'Please will you come every night when it is dull and cloudy and grey and bring some more of your wonderful stars for us?'

The young man smiled and nodded.

'You have earned your reward,' the king told him, 'and we shall look forward to your coming again.'

So after that, every time there was a starless night, the young man went to the palace with a box of fireworks for the princess who loved stars.

Mumbo's Big, Big Ears

Once, in a big country park there lived a very small elephant called Mumbo. Although he was very small – small for an elephant, that is! – Mumbo had an enormous pair of ears and this made him extremely miserable. There were two other elephants, Rajah and Ranee, in the park and their ears were nothing like the size of Mumbo's.

Lots of the children who came to the park would shout,

'Oh, look at *that* elephant. What big *ears* he's got!' and Mumbo would turn away sadly and wish he were small enough to hide somewhere, but of course he wasn't, because even a very small elephant is quite big, really.

Every day Mumbo looked at his reflection in the big lake in the middle of the country park and sighed.

'If only my ears were like Rajah's and Ranee's', he said to himself sadly.

One hot day Mumbo was lying in the shade of some large trees feeling sorry for himself when a lady and three children came along on the other side of the fence.

'Here's a nice cool shady place under these trees,' said the lady. 'We'll sit here for a few minutes before we look at the rest of the animals.'

And they all sat down.

'Please will you tell us a story, Gran?' asked one of the children.

'Yes, *please* Gran,' said the others.

'Oh, all right,' said the lady, smiling, and she began. Of course, Mumbo listened, too. It was the story about a dog with a very short tail who wanted a long tail so that he could wag it to show when he was pleased. He went to see a wizard who said a magic spell:

'Strinkle, stronkle, strunkle, strot,
You aren't pleased with what you've got,
Imble, jimble, jomble, jail,
Soon you'll have a longer tail.'

And the dog's tail grew longer, just as he had wanted.

Mumbo could hardly believe his ears. So *that* was what he needed – a magic spell! But where was he going to find a wizard? He had never seen one in the country park.

He got up and thought hard. Perhaps if he tried the spell the wizard gave the dog in the story it would work on *him*. So he whispered to himself:

'Strinkle, stronkle, strunkle, strot,
You're not pleased with what you've got,
Imble, jimble, jomble, jail,
Soon you'll have two smaller ears.'

Only that didn't sound quite right so he tried again and this time he said:

'Strinkle, stronkle, strunkle, strot
I'm not pleased with what I've got,
Imble, jimble, jomble, jeers,
Soon I'll have two smaller ears.'

And that sounded better. Only his ears didn't feel any smaller.

Mumbo hurried to the lake and looked at his reflection. He didn't look any different. His ears were still enormous. He decided to say the spell again. He closed his eyes and said the words very

slowly and carefully. Then he opened his eyes and looked at his reflection again. He got such a shock that he almost fell into the water because he had two heads – at least he *thought* so, just for a moment, until he realised that the other head belonged to another elephant – an elephant with the biggest, most enormous, most gigantic ears.

'Hallo, I'm Jabombo,' said the huge elephant.

'Jabombo?' repeated Mumbo faintly. 'Not Jabombo the famous elephant who gives rides at the zoo?'

'That's right. Only I'm getting a bit old for all that now so they've sent me to live here. But did I hear some nonsense about your wanting smaller ears?'

Mumbo nodded. 'Like Rajah and Ranee,' he said.

Jabombo threw back his huge head and laughed. 'But their ears are smaller than ours because they're *Indian* elephants,' he said. 'African elephants like us *always* have big ears.' He flapped his own enormous ears proudly.

'Oh,' said Mumbo, 'I didn't know.'

'Well, you can't know everything,' said Jabombo. 'You're still only a very young elephant but a very fine one, too. I shouldn't be surprised if you grow up to be as big and strong as I am.'

Mumbo smiled. 'Oh, I *hope* so!' he said and flapped his big ears happily. He was very glad that the spell hadn't worked, after all.

The Very, Very, Very Long Scarf

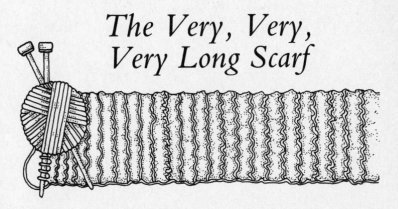

Granny Gibson was very good at two things, knitting and talking. If she was clickety-clicking and clackety-clacking she was happy, so you can imagine how delighted she was when her four grandchildren, Timmy and Susan and Ann and Robert, arrived to stay with her one weekend.

'I'm going to make each of you a scarf for the cold winter days,' she said when they had had their tea. 'I've already started one for Robert – look!' And she showed them the neat rows of knitting on her needles.

'Oh, thank you!' said the children.

That evening they all sat in front of the fire and talked. Of course, Granny Gibson talked more than anyone else. Her tongue clackety-clacked and her knitting needles clickety-clacked, faster and faster. No-one noticed how quickly the knitting was growing and growing until it was nearly bedtime.

Then Susan said, 'Oh, *look*, Gran! Look at your knitting!' and Gran looked and they all looked and then they all started to laugh.

'Oh, my goodness!' said Granny Gibson. 'What a very, very, *very* long scarf!'

'It's long enough for the whole family to use together,' said Robert.

'It's like a giant's skipping-rope!' said Susan.

'It would make a good scarf for a giraffe,' said Ann, remembering the long-necked animals she had seen at the zoo.

'Or a sleeping-bag for a snake,' said Timmy.

'Or a trunk-warmer for an elephant,' said Robert.

'You could embroider "Merry Christmas" on it and fly it from an aeroplane to send greetings to all your friends,' said Timmy, 'then you wouldn't need to send any Christmas cards.'

'Or you could make it into a stocking to hang up on Christmas Eve,' said Ann. 'Just think of all the presents you would get.'

And they all laughed and laughed and laughed until the tears ran down their faces.

'Come on,' said Gran at last, rolling up the very very very long scarf and putting it on her chair. 'Off to bed, all of you. Enough talking –

and knitting – for one night, even for me.'

So the children went up to bed and Gran put the milk bottles on the door-step.

'Brrrrrrrr,' she said to herself, shivering. 'What a cold night.' And she shut the door, switched off the light and *she* went up to bed, as well.

What a surprise she got when she came downstairs next morning. She crept back up and called the children to come quietly and they all tiptoed down into the living-room. Gran pointed to her chair. There, curled up in the middle of the very long scarf was a tiny black kitten. It opened its bright blue eyes and looked at them, then mewed softly.

'Oh, how sweet! But how did it get here?' Ann asked in surprise, 'And whose is it?'

'It looks like a stray,' said Gran, 'It must have crept in last night while I was putting the milk bottles out.'

'Will you keep it?' asked Timmy.

Granny Gibson nodded. 'Yes, perhaps I will.' She chuckled. 'It will be someone to talk to while I'm knitting.'

'Well,' said Susan, 'we thought of lots of things your very very very long scarf could be used for, Gran, but none of us thought of a kitten-cot, did we?'

Knitting

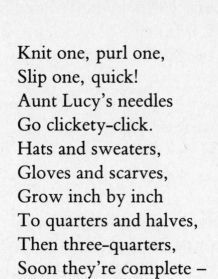

Knit one, purl one,
Slip one, quick!
Aunt Lucy's needles
Go clickety-click.
Hats and sweaters,
Gloves and scarves,
Grow inch by inch
To quarters and halves,
Then three-quarters,
Soon they're complete –
Mittens for hands
And socks for feet.

Knit one, purl one
Knit two together,
Aunt Lucy knits
Whatever the weather.
She knits by the fire,
She knits in the sun
And *always* finishes
What she's begun!
Red wool, green wool,
Purple and black,
Her needles gobble it –
Clackety-clack!

Knit one, purl one
The needles twitch,
Aunt Lucy *never*
Loses a stitch,
Pullover, cardigan,
Bonnet and shawl,
Our Aunt Lucy
Has made them all.
Whether the wool
Is thin or thick,
It's knit one, purl one,
Clickety-click!

The Feast of St Nicholas

Once, across the sea in Holland, in a city called Amsterdam, lived two fair-haired Dutch children. The boy was called Jan and his little sister was called Elly and they lived with their mother and father in a small flat which looked out over a canal.

The children liked to watch boats sail past. Sometimes huge flat barges would chug along. Jan liked to copy the noise they made.

'Tug-tug-tug-tug-tug-tug-tug,' he would say.

But one cold winter morning, the children were *out*side by the canal with their mother and some other children with their mothers, waiting for *another* boat to come along – a very special boat. It was the one bringing Santa Claus – or Sinterklaas as the Dutch children call him – to the city. Jan and Elly and the other children sang songs about him while they waited.

At last Jan shouted, 'Here he is, I can see his red cloak.'

'Hurray!' shouted Elly. 'Yes, here he comes. Oh, doesn't he look grand?'

And he did. He was wearing a red cloak and a red and gold bishop's hat (because St Nicholas was once a bishop in Spain) and he had a gold crook in his hand.

'He has a long white beard,' said Elly. 'He must be a *very* old man.'

As the boat came alongside, Sinterklaas waved and the children waved back, Elly a little shyly.

'Oh, look at Zwarte Piet,' said Jan, laughing.

Zwarte Piet – or Black Peter – was St Nicholas's helper. He was dressed in a green velvet doublet with green stockings and shoes. On his dark curly head he wore a big velvet beret with a huge feather in it. He was dancing about and waving a bundle of birch twigs at the children.

'He always likes to tease,' said mother, laughing.

'Hi, Zwarte Piet,' called all the children.

Zwarte Piet came to the boat rail. 'Have you all been good?' he asked, wagging a finger at them.

'Yes!' shouted all the children.

'All right,' said Zwarte Piet, 'here you are,' and he threw a handful of sweets and little gingerbread nuts called tai-tai to the children.

'Thank you, Zwarte Piet,' they all shouted delightedly and they ran along beside the boat trying to catch more sweets and tai-tai until they came to a small bridge. From here they sang and waved until Sinterklaas and Black Peter were out of sight.

'That was fun,' said Jan, 'and there will be lots more days of fun now, won't there?'

'Oh, yes,' said Mother. 'All the next week until December 5th which is the feast of St Nicholas. That's the day we shall have a party with your cousins and all the family.'

'We'll sing songs and play games, won't we?' asked Elly.

'And give presents,' said Jan, 'and have nice things to eat – spicy biscuits and almond-paste roll. Mmmmmm! Can we go and look in the baker's window now, please, and see all the special things for Sinterklaas?'

'All right,' said Mother.

The baker's shop was on a corner just near the bridge.

'Ooh!' said Jan and Elly, looking at all the rows and rows of things made of coloured marzipan. There were little marzipan houses and animals and fruit and all kinds of other things. They looked lovely.

'Do you think Sinterklaas might bring us a marzipan shape?' asked Elly.

'He might,' said Mother.

That night, before Jan and Elly went to bed, they looked in the cupboard for their clogs. They didn't wear them in town – only when they stayed at their uncle's farm in the country. They weren't going to wear them that night; instead, they each put one outside their bedroom door.

Next day Jan found a green marzipan frog in his and Elly had a little marzipan bear.

'Oh, good old Sinterklaas!' said Jan.

'Can we leave our clogs out again tonight?' asked Elly.

Mother smiled and nodded. For several nights before the feast of St Nicholas children are allowed to leave their clogs or shoes for Sinterklaas to put presents in.

The next night they each got a chocolate letter. Jan got a 'J' and Elly got an 'E'. They were very pleased.

'Sinterklaas is the best time in the whole year,' said Jan.

'Yes, it is,' agreed Elly.

And I think all Dutch children would agree with them, don't you?

The Robin's Carol

A robin sang at Christmas,
Long ago,
A robin sang at Christmas
In rain and snow.

A robin sang at Christmas,
In weather wild,
A robin sang a carol
For the Holy Child.

Little Bear's Growly Day

Little Bear sat in a corner and growled to himself. It didn't sound much of a growl, he thought sadly. When Uncle Bruno growled it sounded so scary that the fur on Little Bear's neck stood up with fear. He trembled just to think of Uncle Bruno's long, loud growl.

'If only *I* could growl like that,' Little Bear said to himself with a sigh. Then he thought, 'Perhaps if I practise hard enough I might be nearly as good as he is, one day.' And he was so pleased with this idea that he decided to start practising there and then.

'Grrrrrrrrrr,' he said. Then he tried to make the sound further down in his throat. 'Grrrrrrrrrr.' Then he made the same noise but ended by opening his mouth as wide as he could, just like Uncle Bruno had done once when he had given his biggest gruffest growl to scare away a prowling wolf.

'Grrrrrrrooooooow,' said Little Bear, 'GrrrrOOOOOOW!'

'That's better,' he said, feeling very pleased with himself and he practised again and again.

Then he decided to go for a walk in the forest and show off his new growl to his friends. He padded along the track and before long he saw his friends the squirrels.

'Grrrrrrrooooooow,' said Little Bear. He was going to say, 'What do you think of my new growl, squirrels?' but all the squirrels had gone scampering away up a tree, chattering. Little Bear was very disappointed.

He went on along the track until he came to the river bank where his friends the otters were playing.

'Grrrrrrrooooooow,' said Little Bear, 'what do you think of my new growl, otters?'

But there wasn't an otter left on the river bank. They had all plunged into the water and were swimming away as fast as they could.

Little Bear watched them sadly then wandered off down the track again. Soon he came to the bushes where his friends the robins had their nest. They were fluttering about from twig to twig.

'Grrrrroooow,' said Little Bear. 'What do you think of my new growl, robins?'

But the robins had flown off twittering loudly before he had finished speaking and without bothering to answer him.

Little Bear felt very unhappy. None of his friends seemed to like him any more. He couldn't think why!

Sadly he walked on along the track. He hadn't gone very far when he saw Uncle Bruno dozing beside some big rocks.

'Grrrrrrrooooooow,' said Little Bear as loudly as he could.

Uncle Bruno got up quickly and gave his long low growl that finished off with a kind of roar.

Little Bear trembled and all his fur stood on end he was so frightened, but he stood quite still and growled again.

'GrrrrrrrroooooooOOOOOW!' he said.

Then Uncle Bruno opened his eyes very wide. 'Is that Little Bear?' he asked in surprise.

Little Bear nodded. 'Yes, Uncle Bruno,' he said.

'Good gracious!' said Uncle Bruno. 'Do you know you frightened the life out of me with that great growl of yours? I didn't know you could growl like that, young fellow.'

Little Bear could hardly believe his ears. 'I've

. . . I've been trying to copy *you*,' he said a little shyly.

'Oh, you have, have you?' said Uncle Bruno, his eyes twinkling.

'Yes,' Little Bear nodded. Then he added sadly, 'But none of my friends seem to like me with my new growl.' And he told Uncle Bruno all about the squirrels and the otters and the robins and how none of them had stayed to listen to his growl.

Uncle Bruno threw back his big furry head and laughed.

'No wonder, Little Bear,' he said, 'they were all terrified of you, like *I* was. You don't use that kind of a growl to greet your friends, Little Bear – that's only to scare away your enemies.'

'Oh,' said Little Bear sadly, 'I didn't know.'

'I'll tell you what, though,' said Uncle Bruno, 'it's the best growl I ever heard from a young bear. You'll be the champion growler in this forest when you're just a bit older and then you'll be able to protect us all, young fellow. Now, off you go back home and tell your mother what I said.'

Little Bear set off happily along the track in the direction of home.

'Hallo, Little Bear,' sang the robins as he passed their bushes.

'Good morning, Little Bear,' called the otters as he passed the river bank.

'Nice to see you, Little Bear,' said the squirrels as he passed their tree.

Little Bear answered them all in his softest growl. He was sorry he couldn't let them hear his *new* growl but they weren't bears so they wouldn't understand. But Uncle Bruno had said that one day he would be the best growler in the forest and Uncle Bruno was a bear who knew all about such things.

Rachel's Dance

Rachel – Rachel Catherine Jones
Danced across the stepping stones,
Over the meadow, light as air,
She danced with rainbows in her hair,
And when she reached the kissing-gate
She danced right through and did not wait!

Through the wood and up the hill,
The hours passed by and she danced still,
As light, as light as thistledown
She danced until the moon shone down,
Then back across the stepping stones
Danced Rachel – Rachel Catherine Jones.

Dusty,
the Water-Mill Cat

Once there was a cat who lived in an old water mill beside a bubbling little stream. She was not a very happy cat because her master, the miller, did not treat her well. He only kept her to catch any rats and mice that came to nibble the grains of wheat and he gave her very little food and hardly any milk. In fact, she wouldn't even have had a name had it not been for Jack, the farmer's boy, who brought cartloads of grain to the mill.

'Hallo, Dusty,' Jack had said, bending down to stroke her the first time he had come to the mill. He called her Dusty because her fur had a fine coating of flour, like everything else inside the mill.

Dusty liked Jack. She looked forward to him coming and the tasty scraps he brought for her to eat.

One morning, Dusty was looking out of the window, watching the water in the stream turn the huge wheel on the side of the mill.

'Plash, plash, plash, plash,' went the wheel as the water pushed it round. As it moved it made lots of other cogs and wheels *inside* the mill creak and turn and these made the machinery work that ground the wheat into flour.

The miller was watching the golden grain pouring into the huge grinders and coming out as fine, white flour and his greedy eyes glinted as he reckoned up how much money he would get for each sack.

Just then there was a tap at the door. The miller frowned as he went to open it. Dusty followed him, curiously.

Outside stood an old woman bent almost double and dressed in rags.

'Please sir, have you a bowl of soup and a crust of bread for a poor old woman?' she begged.

'Certainly not!' cried the miller angrily. 'How dare you come here, wasting my time! Get away, you dirty old good-for-nothing.' And he waved an impatient arm in her face.

The old woman's bright little eyes narrowed.

'You'll be sorry for this,' she said. 'Mean, *mean*, that's what you are. Why, anyone can see that just by looking at that poor half-starved cat of yours.' She nodded towards Dusty. 'But you'll be sorry for your meanness.' She wagged a bony finger at him and went away muttering to herself.

'Silly old fool!' said the miller going back inside.

But Dusty knew that it was the miller who had been a fool. *She* knew, because she was a cat and cats know such things.

A little while later Jack arrived with his cart full of grain.

'You're late!' said the miller crossly. 'Where have you been?'

'I'm sorry,' said Jack, 'but just as I was setting out, a poor old woman came begging for food.'

'You didn't give her any, did you?' asked the miller.

'Of course,' said Jack. 'The poor old thing was hungry.'

Dusty purred to herself. She was glad Jack had been kind to the old woman.

The next day was hot and sunny.

'Phew! It's too hot to work,' grumbled the miller, opening the window wide.

Dusty didn't mind. She liked the sun. She lay on the window ledge and dozed.

The next day was even hotter *and* the next day *and* the next.

'Lovely weather for the harvest,' said Jack happily when he came two weeks later.

'Yes, but there's not much water left in the stream,' said the miller anxiously. He knew that if the stream dried up there would be no water to turn the mill wheel and if the mill wheel didn't turn, neither would any of the other wheels *inside* the mill and if *they* didn't turn, the machinery wouldn't work and that meant the grain couldn't be ground into flour and if there was no flour, *he* wouldn't make any money.

And that is exactly what happened. There was no rain and the stream dried up. Eventually the miller had no money left. But Jack was quite rich after the good harvest. So the miller sold the mill to Jack.

'You can have the cat as well,' said the miller. 'I don't want the good-for-nothing creature. She will be of no use to me now.'

Jack was delighted – so was Dusty. She purred as she followed her new master about the mill.

'We'll soon get the place comfortable,' he told Dusty, 'and back to working order.' He sighed. 'If only it would rain and we could get the wheel turning again,' he said.

At that very moment there was a roll of thunder and huge spots of rain appeared on the window.

'Well!' said Jack, smiling in astonishment. 'Would you believe it? It's like magic!'

Dusty remembered the old woman and purred. She knew it *was* magic!

Flat Cats

Poor cats
That live in flats –
No garden to run in,
No trees to have fun in,
No games
In lanes,
No fights
At nights,
No searching bins
For fish-skins.
No rooftop calling
Or caterwauling
No chasing
Or racing
Up alleys
And snickets
Or prowling
Through thickets
To ensnare bird
Or mouse
Like a cat
From a house.
Poor cats
In flats!

The Boulie Stone

One sunny summer afternoon, a boy was wandering barefoot along a beach. He was on holiday at the seaside and enjoying himself very much, building sandcastles, exploring rockpools and paddling by the sea.

This particular afternoon, the tide was coming in and the boy watched the little waves turning and churning the coloured pebbles on the shore, chasing them higher and higher up the beach. Suddenly, the boy noticed a stone that was bigger and rounder than the others. A wave swept it up the beach and it rolled back to meet the next wave. That one sent it spinning forward again and then, gently, it rolled back down towards the sea.

'*Is* it a stone or is it a ball?' the boy asked himself and ran and picked it up. It was about the size of a tennis ball but it was indeed a stone – a smooth, round stone. He turned it over in his hand. It was grey with a reddish patch on one side and it felt slightly warm.

The boy bowled it along the sandy part of the beach. It rolled a long way. Then he bowled it to the oncoming waves and they bowled it back.

The boy was delighted with the stone. He ran up the beach to where his mother and father and baby sister were sitting.

'Look what I've found!' he called.

'Oh yes, that *is* unusual,' said his mother, taking the stone and examining it.

'How did it get so smooth?' the boy asked.

'Because the sea has turned it over and over so many times,' said his father. 'Any roughness has been worn away.' Then he laughed. 'The sea must have played a *lot* of games with *that* stone.'

Little did any of them know how true those words were! The sea *had* played lots of games with the stone. In fact, it was one of the sea's favourite toys. So when it heard the boy say, 'I think I'll keep it and take it home to show my friends,' the sea was very angry indeed. It turned grey with rage and began to shout:

'Shame! Shame! To steal from the sea –
Give my boulie stone back to me!'

But the boy only heard the smack of the waves as they rushed angrily up the beach and felt the cold spray on his skin. He shivered a little. Only a few minutes ago the sea had been blue. Now it looked so cold.

'Come on, the tide's coming in fast,' said the boy's mother and they made their way back to the cottage where they were staying. When they got there the boy put the stone on the window-sill in his bedroom.

The next day the boy's father had promised to take him on a boat trip. It was a cold, grey day.

'The sea's a bit choppy,' said the owner of the boat as they climbed aboard.

The sea *was* a bit choppy. The boat rocked up and down and from side to side. And sometimes waves splashed right over the side, making pools in the bottom of the boat. The boy didn't like it at all. He felt very frightened and rather sick. He sat clutching a rail and closed his eyes. The roar of the sea was all around. It seemed to be shouting to him:

'Shame! Shame! To steal from the sea –
Give my boulie stone back to me!'

The boy blinked and opened his eyes. What was that? He must have been dreaming. The sea couldn't speak . . . could it? The boat rocked and rocked more violently than ever.

How glad the boy was when they got back to harbour. He didn't ever want to go in a boat again.

When he got back to the cottage he went up to his room and looked at the stone on the window-sill. Of course, he had imagined all that on the boat. It was the seasickness that had made him think the sea was talking to him.

But that night, as he lay in bed, he could hear the wind howling and the boom of breakers down on the shore and in his dreams he heard the crashing waves again that seemed to drum out the message:

'Shame! Shame! To steal from the sea –
Give my boulie stone back to me!'

Suddenly there was a loud crack and the boy woke with a start. What was that noise? Had the cottage been struck by lightning?

Trembling, he reached out and switched on the light. His gaze went at once to the window-sill. The boulie stone wasn't there! It had vanished! He sat up, hardly able to believe it. So it *must* have been bewitched!

Then he saw it, lying on the floor, not far from

his bed. It must have rolled off the windowsill – that was what the noise had been. Probably a draught from the window had blown it off.

Even so, as soon as it was daylight, the boy got up, dressed and tiptoed out of the cottage, clutching the stone in his hand. He made his way down to the beach where the sea was frothing and foaming like a witch's cauldron.

'Shame! Shame! To steal from the sea –
Give my boulie stone back to me!'

it seemed to be scolding.

With all his might the boy hurled the stone as far as he could into the angry sea, then turned and ran back to the cottage.

'It's a funny thing,' said his father at breakfast time, after he had been out to buy a newspaper. 'The sea's been raging all night and yet it's as calm as a millpond now. It's unbelievable how quickly it changes. We'll be able to have another picnic on the beach today.'

'Good,' said the boy's mother. 'You'll be able to look and see if you can find any more round stones.'

She didn't understand why the boy just smiled and shook his head and said he didn't think he would bother!

Fireworks

Whizz! Bang! Popple! Crack!
There goes a zig-zagging Jumping Jack.

And down through the darkness, again and
    again,
Come tumbling showers of Golden Rain.

A rocket goes fizzing into the air,
Now red and green stars are shining there.

And when we light the Catherine Wheel
A dozen colours begin to reel.

Watch out – here's another Jumping Jack!
Whizz! Bang! Popple! Crack!

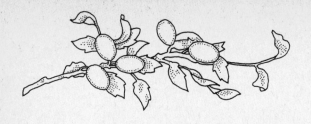

The Damson Tree

Once, in a little orchard, stood a damson tree. In spring, daffodils grew in the grass underneath the tree.

'Oh, how beautiful you are,' sighed the damson tree. 'I wish I were gold, like you.'

'But you are beautiful, too,' said the daffodils. 'Look at all your fine, white lacy blossom.'

The damson tree shook her branches. 'Gold is my favourite colour,' it said.

In summer, hundreds of buttercups flowered in the orchard.

'Oh, how beautiful you are,' said the damson tree.

'But you are very attractive, too,' said the buttercups, 'with your pretty green leaves.'

The damson tree whispered sadly, 'Gold is my favourite colour.'

Sometimes birds came to play hide-and-seek in the branches of the trees in the orchard. The damson tree watched the little goldcrests and the yellowhammers and the yellow wagtails and the goldfinches.

'Oh, how beautiful you are,' sighed the tree.

'But you look very fine, too,' said the birds, 'with your branches laden with purple-blue damsons,' and the goldfinch pecked one of the fruits greedily.

'But gold is my favourite colour,' said the tree sadly.

The sun shone down on the damson tree.

'Oh, how beautiful you are,' said the damson tree. 'I wish I were gold like you.'

'Be patient!' said the sun.

'What do you mean?' asked the damson tree, but the sun just smiled lazily and went on ripening the fruit.

One day the goldfinch came back to peck at a juicy, ripe damson.

'Oh,' said the tree, 'you are so beautiful. I wish *I* were gold like you.'

'But you *are* gold,' said the goldfinch.

'Am I?' asked the damson tree in surprise.

'Yes,' said the goldfinch. 'Haven't you noticed? Your leaves have changed to their autumn colour.'

The damson tree could hardly believe it. It looked at itself. Every leaf was a beautiful golden yellow.